To Celebrate

_____

_____

Date

_____

# THANK YOU FOR COMING.

*Let's celebrate!*

Guest Name

_____

Wishes & Messages

_____

_____

_____

_____

_____

EMAIL/PHONE
_____

Guest Name

_____

Wishes & Messages

_____

_____

_____

_____

_____

_____

EMAIL/PHONE

Guest Name

_____

Wishes & Messages

_____

_____

_____

_____

_____

_____

Email/Phone

## Guest Name

_____

## Wishes & Messages

_____

_____

_____

_____

_____

EMAIL/PHONE _____

*Guest Name*

_____

*Wishes & Messages*

_____

_____

_____

_____

_____

_____

EMAIL/PHONE

Guest Name

_____

Wishes & Messages

_____

_____

_____

_____

_____

_____

Email/Phone

Guest Name
_____

Wishes & Messages

_____
_____
_____
_____
_____
_____

Email/Phone _____

Guest Name

_____

Wishes & Messages

_____

_____

_____

_____

_____

_____

Email/Phone

Guest Name

_____

Wishes & Messages

_____

_____

_____

_____

_____

_____

Email/Phone

## Guest Name

_____

## Wishes & Messages

_____

_____

_____

_____

_____

_____

Email/Phone _____

Guest Name

_____

Wishes & Messages

_____

_____

_____

_____

_____

_____

EMAIL/PHONE
_____

Guest Name

Wishes & Messages

Email/Phone

*Guest Name*

_____

*Wishes & Messages*

_____

_____

_____

_____

_____

_____

EMAIL/PHONE _____

## Guest Name

_____

## Wishes & Messages

_____

_____

_____

_____

_____

_____

Email/Phone

Guest Name

_____

Wishes & Messages

_____

_____

_____

_____

_____

_____

EMAIL/PHONE

## Guest Name

## Wishes & Messages

Email/Phone

# Guest Name

_____

## Wishes & Messages

_____

_____

_____

_____

_____

_____

EMAIL/PHONE _____

# Guest Name

## Wishes & Messages

Email/Phone

*Guest Name*

_____

*Wishes & Messages*

_____

_____

_____

_____

_____

EMAIL/PHONE _____

## Guest Name

_____

### Wishes & Messages

_____

_____

_____

_____

_____

Email/Phone _____

Guest Name

_____

Wishes & Messages

_____

_____

_____

_____

_____

_____

Email/Phone

*Guest Name*

_____

*Wishes & Messages*

_____

_____

_____

_____

_____

_____

EMAIL/PHONE

*Guest Name*

_____

*Wishes & Messages*

_____

_____

_____

_____

_____

_____

EMAIL/PHONE

*Guest Name*

*Wishes & Messages*

Email/Phone

*Guest Name*

_____

*Wishes & Messages*

_____

_____

_____

_____

_____

_____

EMAIL/PHONE

*Guest Name*

*Wishes & Messages*

Email/Phone

Guest Name

_____

Wishes & Messages

_____

_____

_____

_____

_____

_____

Email/Phone

## Guest Name

_____

## Wishes & Messages

_____

_____

_____

_____

_____

Email/Phone
_____

_Guest Name_

_____

_Wishes & Messages_

_____

_____

_____

_____

_____

_____

Email/Phone
_____

Guest Name

_____

Wishes & Messages

_____

_____

_____

_____

_____

_____

Email/Phone
_____

*Guest Name*

*Wishes & Messages*

Email/Phone

*Guest Name*

_____

*Wishes & Messages*

_____

_____

_____

_____

_____

✉ Email/Phone
_____

Guest Name

_____

Wishes & Messages

_____

_____

_____

_____

_____

_____

Email/Phone

Guest Name

_____

Wishes & Messages

_____

_____

_____

_____

_____

_____

Email/Phone

Guest Name

_____

Wishes & Messages

_____

_____

_____

_____

_____

_____

EMAIL/PHONE _____

Guest Name

Wishes & Messages

EMAIL/PHONE

Guest Name

_____

Wishes & Messages

_____

_____

_____

_____

_____

_____

Email/Phone

Guest Name

_____

Wishes & Messages

_____

_____

_____

_____

_____

Email/Phone
_____

Guest Name

_____

Wishes & Messages

_____

_____

_____

_____

_____

_____

EMAIL/PHONE
_____

Guest Name

Wishes & Messages

_____

_____

_____

_____

_____

Email/Phone

Guest Name

_____

Wishes & Messages

_____

_____

_____

_____

_____

_____

Email/Phone

Guest Name

_____

Wishes & Messages

_____

_____

_____

_____

_____

_____

Email/Phone

Guest Name

_____

Wishes & Messages

_____

_____

_____

_____

_____

_____

Email/Phone

Guest Name

_____

Wishes & Messages

_____

_____

_____

_____

_____

Email/Phone

*Guest Name*

_____

*Wishes & Messages*

_____

_____

_____

_____

_____

_____

EMAIL/PHONE _____

Guest Name

_____

Wishes & Messages

_____

_____

_____

_____

_____

_____

EMAIL/PHONE

Guest Name

_____

Wishes & Messages

_____

_____

_____

_____

_____

_____

Email/Phone
_____

## Guest Name

_____

## Wishes & Messages

_____

_____

_____

_____

_____

_____

EMAIL/PHONE

Guest Name

_____

Wishes & Messages

_____

_____

_____

_____

_____

_____

Email/Phone

## Guest Name

_____

## Wishes & Messages

_____

_____

_____

_____

_____

Email/Phone _____

*Guest Name*

_____

*Wishes & Messages*

_____

_____

_____

_____

_____

EMAIL/PHONE

Guest Name

_____

Wishes & Messages

_____

_____

_____

_____

_____

_____

EMAIL/PHONE _____

## Guest Name

_____

## Wishes & Messages

_____

_____

_____

_____

_____

_____

Email/Phone

Guest Name

_____

Wishes & Messages

_____

_____

_____

_____

_____

Email/Phone
_____

*Guest Name*

_____

*Wishes & Messages*

_____

_____

_____

_____

_____

_____

Email/Phone

Guest Name

_____

Wishes & Messages

_____

_____

_____

_____

_____

_____

EMAIL/PHONE

# Guest Name

_____

## Wishes & Messages

_____

_____

_____

_____

_____

Email/Phone

Guest Name

_____

Wishes & Messages

_____

_____

_____

_____

_____

_____

Email/Phone

Guest Name

_____

Wishes & Messages

_____

_____

_____

_____

_____

_____

Email/Phone
_____

Guest Name

_____

Wishes & Messages

_____

_____

_____

_____

_____

_____

EMAIL/PHONE

Guest Name

_____

Wishes & Messages

_____

_____

_____

_____

_____

_____

Email/Phone

_____

*Guest Name*

*Wishes & Messages*

EMAIL/PHONE

Guest Name

_____

Wishes & Messages

_____

_____

_____

_____

_____

_____

Email/Phone

Guest Name

_____

Wishes & Messages

_____

_____

_____

_____

_____

Email/Phone
_____

## Guest Name

_____

## Wishes & Messages

_____

_____

_____

_____

_____

_____

Email/Phone

Guest Name

_____

Wishes & Messages

_____

_____

_____

_____

_____

_____

EMAIL/PHONE

Guest Name

_____

Wishes & Messages

_____

_____

_____

_____

_____

Email/Phone _____

Guest Name

Wishes & Messages

Email/Phone

Guest Name

_____

Wishes & Messages

_____

_____

_____

_____

_____

_____

Email/Phone
_____

## Guest Name

## Wishes & Messages

EMAIL/PHONE

*Guest Name*

_____

*Wishes & Messages*

_____

_____

_____

_____

_____

_____

EMAIL/PHONE

## Guest Name

_____

## Wishes & Messages

_____

_____

_____

_____

_____

_____

EMAIL/PHONE

# Guest Name

## Wishes & Messages

EMAIL/PHONE

## Guest Name

_____

## Wishes & Messages

_____

_____

_____

_____

_____

_____

EMAIL/PHONE

*Guest Name*

_____

*Wishes & Messages*

_____

_____

_____

_____

_____

_____

EMAIL/PHONE

_Guest Name_

_Wishes & Messages_

Email/Phone

Guest Name

_____

Wishes & Messages

_____

_____

_____

_____

_____

_____

Email/Phone

Guest Name

_____

Wishes & Messages

_____

_____

_____

_____

_____

_____

Email/Phone

*Guest Name*

_____

*Wishes & Messages*

_____

_____

_____

_____

_____

Email/Phone _____

*Guest Name*

_____

*Wishes & Messages*

_____

_____

_____

_____

_____

EMAIL/PHONE _____

*Guest Name*

_____

*Wishes & Messages*

_____

_____

_____

_____

_____

_____

EMAIL/PHONE

## Guest Name

_____

## Wishes & Messages

_____

_____

_____

_____

_____

_____

Email/Phone

Guest Name

_____

Wishes & Messages

_____

_____

_____

_____

_____

_____

Email/Phone

Guest Name

_____

Wishes & Messages

_____

_____

_____

_____

_____

Email/Phone _____

## Guest Name

_____

## Wishes & Messages

_____

_____

_____

_____

_____

Email/Phone

Guest Name

_____

Wishes & Messages

_____

_____

_____

_____

_____

_____

Email/Phone

# Guest Name

_____

## Wishes & Messages

_____

_____

_____

_____

_____

_____

EMAIL/PHONE

Guest Name

_____

Wishes & Messages

_____

_____

_____

_____

_____

_____

EMAIL/PHONE

_Guest Name_

_____

_Wishes & Messages_

_____

_____

_____

_____

_____

_____

Email/Phone

## Guest Name

_____

## Wishes & Messages

_____

_____

_____

_____

_____

_____

EMAIL/PHONE

Guest Name

_____

Wishes & Messages

_____

_____

_____

_____

_____

_____

EMAIL/PHONE

*Guest Name*

*Wishes & Messages*

EMAIL/PHONE

*Guest Name*

_____

*Wishes & Messages*

_____

_____

_____

_____

_____

_____

Email/Phone

## Guest Name

_____

## Wishes & Messages

_____

_____

_____

_____

_____

_____

EMAIL/PHONE

_Guest Name_

_Wishes & Messages_

EMAIL/PHONE

Guest Name

_____

Wishes & Messages

_____

_____

_____

_____

_____

Email/Phone

Guest Name

_____

Wishes & Messages

_____

_____

_____

_____

_____

_____

Email/Phone

*Guest Name*

*Wishes & Messages*

EMAIL/PHONE

*Guest Name*

*Wishes & Messages*

EMAIL/PHONE

## Guest Name

_____

## Wishes & Messages

_____

_____

_____

_____

_____

Email/Phone
_____

*Guest Name*

_____

*Wishes & Messages*

_____

_____

_____

_____

_____

EMAIL/PHONE
_____

## Guest Name

_____

## Wishes & Messages

_____

_____

_____

_____

_____

_____

EMAIL/PHONE

Guest Name

_____

Wishes & Messages

_____

_____

_____

_____

_____

_____

EMAIL/PHONE

Guest Name

_____

Wishes & Messages

_____

_____

_____

_____

_____

_____

EMAIL/PHONE

Guest Name

_____

Wishes & Messages

_____

_____

_____

_____

_____

_____

Email/Phone

# NOTES & PHOTOS

# NOTES & PHOTOS

# NOTES & PHOTOS

# NOTES & PHOTOS

# NOTES & PHOTOS

# GIFT LOG

| Name / Email / Phone | Gift |
| --- | --- |
| | |
| | |
| | |
| | |
| | |
| | |
| | |
| | |
| | |
| | |

# GIFT LOG

| Name / Email / Phone | Gift |
|---|---|
| | |
| | |
| | |
| | |
| | |
| | |
| | |
| | |
| | |
| | |
| | |
| | |

# GIFT LOG

| Name / Email / Phone | Gift |
| --- | --- |
| | |
| | |
| | |
| | |
| | |
| | |
| | |
| | |
| | |
| | |
| | |

# GIFT LOG

| Name / Email / Phone | Gift |
|---|---|
| | |
| | |
| | |
| | |
| | |
| | |
| | |
| | |
| | |
| | |
| | |
| | |

# GIFT LOG

| Name / Email / Phone | Gift |
| --- | --- |
| | |
| | |
| | |
| | |
| | |
| | |
| | |
| | |
| | |
| | |
| | |

# GIFT LOG

| Name / Email / Phone | Gift |
| --- | --- |
| | |
| | |
| | |
| | |
| | |
| | |
| | |
| | |
| | |
| | |
| | |
| | |

# GIFT LOG

| Name / Email / Phone | Gift |
| --- | --- |
| | |
| | |
| | |
| | |
| | |
| | |
| | |
| | |
| | |
| | |
| | |

CPSIA information can be obtained
at www.ICGtesting.com
Printed in the USA
LVHW021937280623
751017LV00004B/50